My Personal Financial Planner
For Use with Personal Finance

Eleventh Edition

E. Thomas Garman
Professor Emeritus, Virginia Tech University

Raymond E. Forgue
University of Kentucky

SOUTH-WESTERN
CENGAGE Learning

Australia • Brazil • Japan • Korea • Mexico • Singapore • Spain • United Kingdom • United States

For product information and technology assistance, contact us at **Cengage Learning Academic Resource Center, 1-800-423-0563**.

For permission to use material from this text or product, submit all requests online at **www.cengage.com/permissions**. Further permissions questions can be emailed to **permissionrequest@cengage.com**.

ISBN-13: 978-1-111-82562-1
ISBN-10: 1-111-82562-9

South-Western Cengage Learning
2640 Eagan Woods Drive Suite 220
Eagan, MN 55121

Cengage Learning is a leading provider of customized learning solutions with office locations around the globe, including Singapore, the United Kingdom, Australia, Mexico, Brazil, and Japan. Locate your local office at: **international.cengage.com/region**.

Cengage Learning products are represented in Canada by Nelson Education, Ltd.

For your course and learning solutions, visit **www.cengage.com**.

Purchase any of our products at your local college store or at our preferred online store **www.CengageBrain.com**.

Printed in the United States of America
1 2 3 4 5 6 7   15 14 13 12 11

PREFACE

All the financial knowledge you will gain in your study of personal finance will be of little use if you do not put it into practice. *My Personal Financial Planner* takes all of the major financial planning tools from *Personal Finance*, 11th edition and makes them real for you, and in a genuinely meaningful and personal way. We have converted the tools into forms, calculators and worksheets that you can use for years to come to develop your own financial plans and successfully manage your own financial life. We want you to be truly successful in your personal finances *throughout* your life. Reading *Personal Finance* will give you a big head start. Using *My Personal Financial Planner* will give you additional support because it will personalize personal finance for you.

"Your" *My Personal Financial Planner* is organized according to the five-part structure of *Personal Finance*.

►**Financial Planning** We first deal with the basics of financial planning. Here you will prepare your own financial statements, calculate your financial ratios and be able to make almost any type of time value of money calculation imaginable.

►**Money Management** The second section of the workbook focuses on money management and covers income taxes, banking, credit, and the purchase of vehicles and a home. Using these worksheets will save you literally thousands of dollars in taxes, bank fees, interest, and dollars not spent for "big-tickets" items that you buy. That's real money, and these savings will help you along on your road to financial success.

►**Income and Asset Protection** The third section focuses on income and asset protection and specifically on insurance as the primary mechanism for that protection. These worksheets will help you buy the right insurance coverage and make the most of your insurance dollar. If you don't waste money, it is yours to keep for spending, saving or investing.

►**Investments** The fourth section of the workbook covers investments. It walks you through the subject of investments using worksheets and forms to help you clarify your thinking about investing successfully for your future. It gives you the tools you absolutely must put in place in your investment program so that you will build the wealth you will need to reach your most ambitious financial goals.

►**Retirement and Estate Planning** The fifth section of *My Personal Financial Planner* focuses on retirement and estate planning. Here you will be able to set in motion–early in your full-time working career--the steps to build the multi-million-dollar financial nest-egg for a secure retirement. Yes, you can build that kind of financial success. To do so, you must start early and sacrifice some spending so you can save and invest to support your future lifestyle. This section of worksheets and forms also will help you prepare for the distribution of your estate in ways that meet your desires. There are some simple steps that you can take, and the forms and worksheets will guide you along that path.

We encourage you to make use of this special workbook as you study *Personal Finance*. Your efforts will help you visualize and really understand the practical aspects of what you are learning while you read *Personal Finance*. Your efforts will make that knowledge richer and deeper, and totally personal to you. That's what "personal" in *Personal Finance* is all about! The forms and worksheets in *My Personal Financial Planner* will aid in your success in class, but more than that they will improve your genuine personal financial success throughout your lifetime.

NOTE: Many of the worksheets in this workbook including interactive calculators can also be found on the Garman/Forgue companion website. These items have an asterisk in the list below. Visit the *Garman/Forgue* companion website at www.cengagebrain.com.

TABLE OF CONTENTS

SECTION THREE   56

INCOME AND ASSET PROTECTION   56

SECTION FOUR   65

INVESTMENTS   65

SECTION FIVE   82

RETIREMENT AND ESTATE PLANNING   82

SECTION ONE

FINANCIAL PLANNING

This section of your workbook focuses on the basics of the study of personal finances and begins your efforts in financial planning. Each worksheet will allow you to think through a decision or perform calculations related to a specific area of personal financial management in a way that has direct benefit to you. Worksheets marked with an asterisk can be found on the Garman/Forgue companion website. Visit **www.cengagebrain.com.**

WORKSHEET 1—TRACKING THE ECONOMY

The success of your personal financial plans will depend upon your understanding of the current state of the economy as measured by several key statistics. You will also want to be able to predict the movement of those statistics over the next one or two years. This worksheet will provide a way for you to record these key statistics for reference as you make your financial plans. For each statistic, we have included a website that will provide the information you will need. Your forecasts can also be based on your reading of economic news in your local newspaper, weekly news magazines, and financial periodicals such as the *Wall Street Journal*. (Use with *Personal Finance*, 11th edition, pages 6-13.)

Tracking the Economy Worksheet

Key economic statistic	Current data	Your forecast for one year from now	Your forecast for two years from now
Inflation rate—consumer price index (www.bls.gov)			
Inflation rate—producer price index (www.bls.gov)			
Federal funds rate (www.federalreserve.gov)			
30-year mortgage interest rate (www.bankrate.com)			
1-year certificate of deposit rate (www.bankrate.com)			
5-year certificate of deposit rate (www.bankrate.com)			
T-bill constant maturity rate (www.treasurydirect.gov)			
Index of leading economic indicators (http://www.conference-board.org/data/bci.cfm)			
Rate of change in the gross domestic product (www.bea..gov)			

WORKSHEET 2—CALCULATING THE FUTURE VALUE OF A LUMP SUM

One of the most common questions that people ask about their investments and savings is "How much money will I have in x years?" An example might be someone who earns a bonus at work and wants to save it for five years. In personal finance language, he or she wants to know the future value of a lump sum. This worksheet can be used in conjunction with Appendix A.1 in your text to answer this question if you know the amount to be invested, the time period, and the rate of return or interest on the investment. An interactive calculator that performs this same procedure can be found on the Garman/Forgue companion website. (Use with *Personal Finance*, 11th edition, pages 16-21.)

Future Value of a Lump-sum Worksheet

(A) Lump sum to be invested or saved	(B) Time period that the funds will be invested	(C) Rate of return on the invested funds	(D) Factor from Appendix A.1 that corresponds to Items B and C	(E) Future value (A x D)

WORKSHEET 3—CALCULATING THE FUTURE VALUE OF AN ANNUITY

Another common question that people ask about their investments is "How much money will I have in x years if I put a certain amount away each year?" An example might be someone who puts $3,000 into an IRA account each year. In personal finance language, this person wants to know the future value of an annuity. This worksheet can be used in conjunction with Appendix A.3 in your text to answer this question if you know the amount to be invested, the time period, and the rate of return or interest on the investment. An interactive calculator that performs this same procedure can be found on the Garman/Forgue companion website. (Use with *Personal Finance*, 11th edition, pages 16-21.)

Future Value of An Annuity Worksheet

(A) Amount to be invested or saved each year (the annuity)	(B) Time period that the funds will be invested	(C) Rate of return on the invested funds	(D) Factor from Appendix A.3 that corresponds to Items B and C	(E) Future value (A x D)

WORKSHEET 4—CALCULATING THE PRESENT VALUE OF A LUMP SUM

Another common question that people ask about their investments and savings is "How much money will I have to put away now to reach some goal?" An example might be someone wanting to save for a down payment on a home in five years. In personal finance language, he or she wants to know the present value of a lump sum. This worksheet can be used in conjunction with Appendix A.2 in your text to answer this question if you know the amount to be invested, the time period, and the rate of return or interest on the investment. An interactive calculator that performs this same procedure can be found on the Garman/Forgue companion website.   (Use with *Personal Finance*, 11th edition, pages 16-21.)

Present Value of a Lump-sum Worksheet

(A) Lump sum needed	(B) Time period that the funds will be invested	(C) Rate of return on the invested funds	(D) Factor from Appendix A.2 that corresponds to Items B and C	(E) Present value (A x D)

WORKSHEET 5—CALCULATING THE PRESENT VALUE OF AN ANNUITY

Another question that people ask about their investments and savings is "How much money will I need to save so that withdrawing a certain amount each year will allow the money to last *x* years?" An example might be someone who wants to know how large a retirement fund they would need to ensure that the money might last twenty years given a certain rate of withdrawal. In personal finance language, the person wants to know the present value of an annuity. This worksheet can be used in conjunction with Appendix A.4 in your text to answer this question if you know the amount to be invested, the time period, and the rate of return or interest on the investment. An interactive calculator that performs this same procedure can be found on the Garman/Forgue companion website.   (Use with *Personal Finance*, 11th edition, pages 16-21.)

Present Value of An Annuity Worksheet

(A) Amount of money annuity to be received or withdrawn each year	(B) Time period that the funds will be withdrawn	(C) Rate of return on the invested funds	(D) Factor from Appendix A.4 that corresponds to Items B and C	(E) Present value (A x D)

WORKSHEET 6—WHAT IS YOUR WORK STYLE PERSONALITY

Your work-style personality is a unique set of ways of working with and responding to your job requirements, surroundings, and associates. When making a career selection, you must balance your work-style personality against the demands of the work environment. The table below allows you rate the importance of various factors. Rate how you value the following work values as either very important in your choice of career, somewhat important in your choice of career, or unimportant in your choice of career. (Use with *Personal Finance*, 11th edition, page 41.)

	Your Rating of Importance		
Work-Style Factor	**Very Important**	**Somewhat Important**	**Unimportant**
1. Work Conditions			
Independence and autonomy			
Time flexibility			
Change and variety			
Change and risk			
Stability and security			
Physical challenge			
Physical demands			
Mental challenge			
Pressure and time deadlines			
Precise work			
Decision making			

2.   **Work Purposes**

Truth and knowledge			
Expertise and authority			
Esthetic appreciation			
Social conditions			
Material gain			
Achievement and recognition			
Ethical and moral			
Spiritual and transpersonal			

3.   **Work Relationships**

Working alone			
Public contact			
Close friendships			
Group membership			
Helping others			
Influencing others			
Supervising others			
Controlling others			

WORKSHEET 7—MY CAREER FIELD RESEARCH

Selecting a career field should be based on solid research. It helps to have a set of questions prepared in advance. Use this worksheet to gather data about one or more career fields and use the results to compare fields against your values and interests. Various sources of data for your research are located throughout Chapter 2. (Use with *Personal Finance*, 11th edition, page 37-39.)

Career field	
General nature of work performed	
Working conditions such as typical hours, degree of travel required, physical activities, and work locations and surroundings	
Educational level, certifications, and training required for an entry-level position	

Typical career ladder including any geographical relocations that are likely to be required as one advances up the ladder	
Educational level, certifications, and training required for career advancement	
Earnings initially and as career progresses	
Typical employee benefits provided	
Career field outlook in terms of employment growth and likely technological advances	

WORKSHEET 8—COMPARING SALARY OFFERS IN TWO DIFFERENT CITIES

Comparing salary offers from two different cities can be difficult because the cost of living varies across the United States. You can use this worksheet and data from the cityrating.com's website to adjust offers you might receive from prospective employers. An interactive calculator that performs this same procedure can be found on the Garman/Forgue companion website. (Use with *Personal Finance*, 11th edition, page 56-57.)

Comparing Salary Offers Worksheet

(A) City	(B) Salary offer	(C) Estimate of the value of employee benefits	(D) Total compensation package	(E) Cost of Living Index*	(F) Salary adjusted for the cost of living (D/E)

*http://www.cityrating.com/costofliving.asp

WORKSHEET 9—ASSESSING THE BENEFITS OF A SECOND INCOME

While a second income might appear to be a way to get ahead financially, there are some extra considerations that may diminish the benefits. The second income will be taxed at the household's marginal tax rate. And, there are additional expenses for meals, transportation, childcare and other considerations. This worksheet can provide you with a better estimate of the actual contribution of a second income. An interactive calculator that performs this same procedure can be found on the Garman/Forgue companion website. (Use with *Personal Finance*, 11th edition, page 46.)

Decision Making Worksheet	Assessing the Benefits of a Second Income	
	Example	Your Figures
1. Second Income		
Annual Earnings	$30,000	
Value of Benefits	$300.00	
Total	$30,300.00	
2. Expenses		
Federal Income Taxes*	$7,500.00	
State/local Income Taxes*	$1,800.00	
Social Security Taxes	$2,295.00	
Transportation and Commuting	$2,000.00	
Childcare	$3,200.00	
Lunches Out	$1,000.00	
Work Wardrobe	$1,200.00	
Other Work-related Expenses	$300.00	
Take-out food for Supper	$1,200.00	
Guilt Complex Purchases	$600.00	
Total	$21,095.00	
3. Net Value of Second Income		
Total Second Income	$30,300.00	
Total Second Income Expenses	$21,095.00	
Net Amount of Second Income	$9,205.00	

*Your Federal Marginal Tax Rate	25.00%	
*Your State/local Marginal Tax Rate	6.00%	

WORKSHEET 10—MY BALANCE SHEET

A balance sheet provides a snapshot look at your financial status as of a particular date. The result is an accurate assessment of your net worth. You can use this worksheet to determine your assets, liabilities, and resulting net worth. If you complete a worksheet like this once per year, you will see an ongoing picture of your financial progress. An interactive calculator that performs this same procedure can be found on the Garman/Forgue companion website. (Use with *Personal Finance*, 11th edition, pages 70-72.)

My Balance Sheet

Date: _____   Your Name: _____

ASSETS		LIABILITIES	
Monetary Assets			
		Short-term Liabilities	
Cash	_____	Credit card #1	_____
Checking account #1	_____	Credit card #2	_____
Checking account #2	_____	Credit card #3	_____
Savings account #1	_____	Credit card #4	_____
Savings account #2	_____	Medical debts	_____
Savings account #3	_____	Past due utilities	_____
Certificate of deposit #1	_____	Past due rent	_____
Certificate of deposit #2	_____	Personal loans	_____
Money market account	_____	Other	_____
Other	_____	Other	_____
Other	_____	Other	_____
		Total Short-term Liabilities	
Total Monetary Assets	_____		_____
Tangible Assets		**Long-term Liabilities**	_____
Vehicle #1	_____	Vehicle loan #1	_____
Vehicle #2	_____	Vehicle loan #2	_____
Home #1	_____	Home mortgage #1	_____
Home #2	_____	Home mortgage #2	_____
Clothing	_____	Student loan(s)	_____
Furniture	_____	Furniture loans	_____
Entertainment electronics	_____	Computer loans	_____
Home appliances & equipment	_____	Home appliance loans	_____
Computer equipment	_____	Personal loans	_____
Computer software	_____	Other	_____
Jewelry	_____	Other	_____
Recreation items			
Personal property	_____	**Total Long-term Liabilities**	_____
Other tangible assets	_____		
	_____	**TOTAL LIABILITIES**	_____
Total Tangible Assets	_____		
Investment Assets	_____	**MY NET WORTH**	_____
Stocks			
	_____		

Bonds   _____
Mutual fund #1   _____
Mutual fund #2   _____
Employer Retirement account(s)   _____
IRA Accounts   _____
Life ins. cash value(s)   _____
Real estate investments   _____
Collectibles   _____
Other investment assets   _____

Total Investment Assets   _____

TOTAL ASSETS   _____

WORKSHEET 11—MY CASH-FLOW STATEMENT

The key to getting ahead financially is to spend less than you earn. As a college student, that might be difficult, but ignoring the reality of your cash flows in and out is no solution. You can start by keeping track of your spending and income for one month. Then use this worksheet to summarize your spending and income into a cash-flow statement for the month. Assembling your statements over the course of a year will enable you to construct an annual statement. An interactive calculator that performs this same procedure can be found on the Garman/Forgue companion website. (Use with *Personal Finance*, 11th edition, pages 72-76.)

My Cash-flow Statement

Name			
	Insert Your Figures		Insert Your Figures
INCOME		*EXPENSES*	
		FIXED EXPENSES	
Wages #1 (gross)		Rent/Mortgage	
Wages #2 (gross)		Home Insurance	
Interest Income		Real Estate Taxes	
Dividend Income		Vehicle Loan #1	
Sales Commissions		Vehicle Loan #2	
Bonuses		Automobile Insurance	
Tips		Life Insurance	
Gifts		Medical Insurance	
Tax Refunds		Retirement Fund #1	
Other		Retirement Fund #2	
Other		Student Loan Payments	
TOTAL INCOME		Federal Income Tax	
		State Income Taxes	
		City Income Taxes	
		Social Security Taxes	
		Personal Property Taxes	
		Savings #1	
		Savings #2	
		Savings #3	
		Other	
		Other	
		Other	
		Total Fixed Expenses	

		VARIABLE EXPENSES	
		Food (home)	
		Food (meals away)	
		Food (for entertainment)	
		Entertainment	
		Electricity	
		Natural Gas	
		Water/Sewer	
		Garbage Collection	
		Cable TV	
		Local Telephone	
		Long Distance	
		Cell Phone	
		Medical	
		Clothing	
		Gifts	
		Personal Care	
		Personal Allowances	
		Gasoline	
		Vehicle Maintenance	
		Education Expenses	
		Charitable Contributions	
		Other	
		Other	
		Other	
		Other	
		Miscellaneous	
		Total Variable Expenses	
		TOTAL EXPENSES	
		SURPLUS (DEFICIT)	

WORKSHEET 12—MY FINANCIAL RATIOS

The information contained in your balance sheet and your cash-flow statement is a valuable tool for keeping track of and understanding your personal finances. It is also important to use several financial ratios to bring your financial status and behavior into clear focus. The information for these ratios can be found in your balance sheet and cash-flow statement from Worksheets 10 and 11. The ratios are provided below. An interactive calculator that performs these same procedures can be found on the Garman/Forgue companion website. (Use with *Personal Finance*, 11th edition, pages 77-79.)

The **liquidity ratio** tells the number of months that you could continue to meet your expenses using only your monetary assets if all income ceases. Experts recommend that people have monetary assets equal to three to six months' expenses in emergency cash reserves.

Liquidity Ratio

(A) Monetary assets	(B) Monthly expenses	(C) Basic liquidity ratio (A divided by B)

The **asset-to-debt ratio** tells whether you are solvent; your assets exceed your liabilities. An asset-to-debt ratio of more than 1.0 indicates that you are solvent and have a positive net worth.

Asset-to-Debt Ratio

(A) Total assets	(B) Total debt	(C) Asset-to-debt ratio (A divided by B)

The **debt service-to-income ratio** compares your total annual debt payments (including home mortgage debt) with your gross annual income. A debt service-to-income ratio in excess of 0.36 indicates that you are carrying too much debt.

Debt Service-to-Income Ratio

(A) Annual debt repayments	(B) Gross income	(C) Debt service-to-income ratio (A divided by B)

The **debt payments-to-disposable income ratio** compares your monthly nonmortgage debt payments to your monthly disposable income. A debt service-to-disposable income ratio in excess of 0.16 indicates that you are carrying too much nonmortgage debt.

Debt Payments-to-Disposable Income Ratio

(A) Monthly nonmortgage debt payments	(B) Disposable income	(C) Debt payments-to-disposable income ratio (A divided by B)

The **investment assets-to-total assets ratio** provides a good indicator of the degree to which investment assets comprise your total assets. The higher the ratio, the more you are on your way to achieving real wealth.

Investment Assets-to-Total Assets Ratio

(A) Investment assets	(B) Total assets	(C) Investment assets-to-total assets ratio (A divided by B)

WORKSHEET 13—MY FINANCIAL RECORDS

As an effective personal financial planner, you will want to have a system for storing your important documents and records. These documents should be both accessible and secure. It is often wise to keep copies in a file cabinet so they can be accessible and originals in a safe-deposit box, home safe, or other secure location. (Use with *Personal Finance*, 11th edition, pages 79-82.)

Financial Records Worksheet

Item	Location (indicate *copy* or *original* document)		
	Home file	Safe-deposit box	Other
Financial Statements			
Balance sheets for past several years			
Cash flow statements for current and past year			
Written goal statements			
Budgets for current and past year			
Credit control sheet			
Cash-flow calendar for current year			
Personal Documents			
Birth certificate			
Social Security card			
Marriage certificate			
Divorce documents			
Health history			
Record of alimony paid or received			
Record of child support paid or received			
Passport			
Banking and Credit Documents			
Checking and saving account contracts			
Checking and saving account statements			
Certificates of deposit			
Money market/asset management account statements			
Loan agreements/contracts			
Credit card monthly statements			
Insurance Documents			
Automobile insurance policies			
Homeowners insurance policies			
Home inventory			
Health insurance policy or plan description			
Life insurance policies			
Cash value life insurance annual statements			
Insurance claims records			

Item	Home file	Safe-deposit box	Other
Home Ownership Records			
Deed and title documents			
Mortgage contract			
Home repair records			
Home improvement records			
Home owner's warranty contract			
Annual escrow account statements			
Annual mortgage interest statements			
Vehicle Ownership Records			
Vehicle titles			
Vehicle lease agreements			
Vehicle warranty contracts			
Major repair records and receipts			
Tax Documents			
Federal, state, and local returns for past three years			
Older federal, state, and local returns			
Record of work-related child care expenses			
Record of flexible spending accounts			
W-4 forms and pay stubs			
Record of all correspondence with the IRS			
Investment Documents			
Brokerage account agreements			
Brokerage account statements			
Mutual fund account contracts			
Employer defined-benefit plan documents			
Employer defined-contribution plan documents			
IRA and Keogh plan documents			
Mutual fund account statements			
Stock dividends reports			
Inventory and appraisals of collectibles			
Estate Planning Documents			
Wills and Letters of Last Instructions			
List of joint-ownership designations for bank accounts and other assets			
Living Wills and durable powers of attorney			
Financial and medical power of attorney documents			
Trust account agreements and statements			

WORKSHEET 14—MONTHLY SAVINGS NEEDED TO REACH MY FINANCIAL GOALS

Financial goals must be specific in terms of dollar amount, time, and the interim short-term goals that will lead to their achievement. Effective financial planners write their goals down. This worksheet provides a mechanism for you to compile your goals. You then can build your monthly savings needed to reach the goal into your budget (see Worksheet 17). An interactive calculator that performs this same procedure can be found on the Garman/Forgue companion website. (Use with *Personal Finance*, 11th edition, pages 82-85.)

My Financial Goals Worksheet

(A) Describe the goal	(B) Dollar amount required	(C) Deadline date	(D) Date to start saving	(E) Number of months to save (E – D)	(F) Monthly savings amount (from web calculator)

WORKSHEET 15—DETERMINING MONTHLY BUDGET AMOUNTS FOR MY NON-MONTHLY EXPENSES

Allowing for non-monthly expenses is one of the most difficult aspects of budgeting for people who are new to the task. You might have expenses for college tuition, auto insurance, vehicle maintenance, and other items that occur some months and not others. Your best approach is to determine an equivalent monthly amount for each and then include it as a budgeted amount every month. You then can carry over any unspent amounts from month to month to build up a fund to pay the expense in the month that it does occur. The worksheet below can be used to identify these expenses and their monthly allocation. (Use with *Personal Finance*, 11th edition, pages 85-86.)

Determining Monthly Budget Amounts for My Non-monthly Expenses Worksheet

(A) Expense item	(B) Estimated annual expense	(C) Divide by	(D) Estimate monthly allocation (B/C)
Automobile insurance		12	
Homeowners insurance		12	
Life insurance		12	
Other irregular insurance expenses		12	
School tuition		12	
School books and supplies		12	
Other irregular education expenses		12	
Vehicle license renewal and tax		12	
Vehicle maintenance		12	
Vehicle repairs		12	
Other irregular vehicle expenses		12	
Vacations		12	
Holiday gifts		12	
Real estate taxes		12	
Home repair and maintenance		12	
Other irregular housing expenses		12	
Other		12	
Other		12	
Other		12	

WORKSHEET 16—MY REVOLVING SAVINGS FUND

Over the course of a year you will have certain months where an unusually large expenditure might need to be made. Perhaps it will be for a vacation, payment of school expenses, holiday gifts, or for insurance premiums. A revolving savings fund provides a mechanism for setting aside funds for these events. Worksheet 16 builds on Worksheet 15 to provide you with the total amounts you would need to set aside monthly and the cumulative totals that would need to go into your own revolving savings fund. (Use with *Personal Finance*, 11th edition, page 87.)

My Revolving Savings Fund Worksheet

(A) Month	(B) Expense item	(C) Amount needed	(D) Deposit into the fund	(E) Withdrawal from the fund	(F) Fund balance
Jan.					
Feb.					
Mar.					
Apr.					
May					
June					
July					
Aug.					
Sept.					
Oct.					
Nov.					
Dec.					
Total					

WORKSHEET 17—MY BUDGET

Spending less than you earn is the way to get ahead financially. But it does not happen automatically. You need to plan your spending and your income so that you can reach your financial goals. Such a plan is called a budget. The basic idea would be to prepare a budget for a month based on the cash-flow statement for the previous month that you prepared in Worksheet 10. In addition, your budget should be based on the cash-flow statement and your goals list you prepared in Worksheet 14 and provide a monthly allocation for your non-monthly expenses such as insurance. Then you would put the budget into action. Once the month is over you can prepare a new cash-flow statement for that month. Finally, you would prepare a new budget for the next month based on what you learned from living out the first month's budget. This may sound like quite a bit of work but the benefits from developing these sound financial habits will pay off handsomely in the coming years. An interactive calculator that performs this same procedure can be found on the Garman/Forgue companion website. (Use with *Personal Finance*,11th edition, pages 82-94.)

My Budget

Month: _____   **Your Name:** _____

INCOME
- Wages #1 (gross)   _____
- Wages #2 (gross)   _____
- Interest income   _____
- Dividend income   _____
- Sales commissions   _____
- Bonuses   _____
- Tips   _____
- Gifts

- Tax refunds   _____

- Other   _____
- Other   _____

TOTAL INCOME   _____

EXPENDITURES

Fixed Expenses
- Rent/mortgage payment   _____
- Home insurance   _____
- Real estate taxes   _____
- Vehicle loan #1   _____
- Vehicle loan #2

- Automobile insurance   _____

Variable Expenses
- Food (home)   _____
- Food (away)   _____
- Food (entertainment)   _____
- **Entertainment**   _____
- Electricity   _____
- **Natural gas**   _____
- **Water/sewer**   _____

- Garbage collection   _____

- Cable TV
- Local telephone   _____
- Long distance   _____
- Cell phone

          _____

- Medical   _____

- Clothing   _____

- Gifts   _____
- Personal care   _____
- Personal allowances   _____
- Gasoline   _____
- Vehicle maintenance   _____

- Education expenses
- Charitable Contributions   _____

Life insurance _____

Other
Medical insurance _____ Other _____
Retirement fund #1

Other _____
Retirement fund #2 _____

Other
Student loan payments _____

Other _____
Miscellaneous _____

Federal income taxes _____ **Total Variable Expenses** _____

State income taxes _____ _____

City income taxes _____ _____

Social Security taxes _____ _____

Personal property taxes _____ _____
Savings #1 _____ _____
Savings #2 _____
Savings #3

Other _____ _____
Other _____ _____

Other _____ _____

_____

Total Fixed Expenses _____ **TOTAL EXPENDITURES** _____

NET GAIN(LOSS)

_____

WORKSHEET 18—MY BUDGET CATEGORY LEDGER WORKSHEETS

Budgeting entails more than simply preparing a budget. You also have to use the budget to monitor and control spending. To do so you must have some type of recording or ledger system that allows you to keep track of how you are doing in each budget category as the month progresses. Worksheet 18 provides an example ledger sheet you can use. You could set up a page like this in a small spiral notebook—one page for each of your budget categories. (Use with *Personal Finance*, 11th edition, pages 90-94.)

My Budget Category Ledger Worksheets

Budget category and amount budgeted for the month (example: groceries; $150):		
(A) **Date**	**(B)** **Expenditure amount**	**(C)** **Balance remaining** **(Previous balance remaining** **minus Item B)**
Initial budgeted amount plus any carry over from previous month	n/a	$150
Total		

SECTION 2

MONEY MANAGEMENT

This section of your workbook focuses on managing money, credit and spending. Each worksheet will allow you to think through a decision or perform calculations related to a specific area of personal financial management in a way that has direct benefit to you. Worksheets marked with an asterisk can be found on the Garman/Forgue website. Visit www.cengagebrain.com.

WORKSHEET 19—MY SOURCES OF TAXABLE INCOME

It is smart to keep track of your various income sources throughout the tax year so that you will not forget to report them to the Internal Revenue Service. Omitted income could possibly result in an IRS audit and penalties may be assessed on top of the income taxes actually owed.

Use the worksheet below to record all income sources. Record the names of the income sources in the spaces provided. Record the amounts in the appropriate spaces. (Use with *Personal Finance*, 11th edition, pages 108-113).

Sources of Income Worksheet

Type of Income	Source 1: _____	Source 2: _____	Source 3: _____	Source 4: _____	Source 5: _____
Salary	$	$	$	$	$
Wages	$	$	$	$	$
Tips	$	$	$	$	$
Commissions	$	$	$	$	$
Bonuses	$	$	$	$	$
Scholarship for room, board, and other living expenses	$	$	$	$	$
Grants and the value of tuition reductions received for teaching or other services	$	$	$	$	$
Business income	$	$	$	$	$
Capital gains	$	$	$	$	$
Interest and dividends	$	$	$	$	$
Alimony	$	$	$	$	$
Other income	$	$	$	$	$
Other income	$	$	$	$	$

WORKSHEET 20—ESTIMATING MY INCOME TAX LIABILITY AND REFUND OR AMOUNT OWED

Taxable income is calculated by taking the taxpayer's gross income, subtracting any adjustments to income, subtracting either the standard deduction or total itemized deductions, and subtracting the amount permitted for the number of exemptions allowed. The amount of taxable income is then used to determine the taxpayer's liability via the tax tables or tax-rate schedules combined with the appropriate filing status. Use the worksheet below to determine an estimate of your income tax liability (for either last year or next year).

Go online to obtain the amounts for standard deduction, exemption value, and tax tables or tax rate schedules, as well as possible adjustments to income and itemized deductions. Perhaps use figures from YahooFinance Tax Center (finance.yahoo.com/taxes/, CCH (finance.cch.com), or the Internal Revenue Service (irs.gov).

Record your figures in Column C. Step 1: Record your gross income. Step 2: Record any adjustments to gross income. Step 3: Subtract Step 2 from Step 1. Step 4: Record amount of standard deduction or total of itemized deductions. Step 5: Subtract Step 4 from Step 3. Step 6: Record the value of an exemption. Step 7: Subtract Step 6 from Step 5. Step 8: Record tax liability from appropriate tax table or tax rate schedule. Step 9: Record amount of any tax credits. Step 10: Subtract Step 9 from Step 8. An interactive calculator that performs this same procedure can be found on the Garman/Forgue companion website. (Use with *Personal Finance*, 11th edition, pages 108-123.)

Income Tax Liability Worksheet

(A) Steps	(B) Instructions	(C) Your figures
Step 1	Record your gross income.	
Step 2	Record any adjustments to gross income.	
Step 3	Subtract Step 2 from Step 1; the result is your adjusted gross income (AGI).	
Step 4	Record amount of standard deduction or total of itemized deductions.	
Step 5	Subtract Step 4 from Step 3; the result is a subtotal.	
Step 6	Record the total value of your exemptions.	
Step 7	Subtract Step 6 from Step 5; the result is taxable income.	
Step 8	Record tax liability from appropriate tax table or tax rate schedule; result is your final tax liability (if you do not have any tax credits to subtract).	
Step 9	Record amount of any tax credits.	
Step 10	Subtract Step 9 from Step 8; result is your final tax liability.	
Step 11	Record Federal income taxes withheld by employer(s)	

Step 12	Record estimated tax payments made during the year	
Step 13	Subtract Steps 11 and 12 from Step 10; result is (Refund to be Received) or Payment Owed	

WORKSHEET 21—DETERMINING WHETHER I SHOULD FILE FOR A REFUND

You must file a federal income tax return each year if your income meets certain thresholds based on your filing status. But what if you are not required to file a return? The answer is "yes, you should file" if you have a refund coming. That is, if you had more taxes withheld from your paychecks than you ultimately owed. (Use with *Personal Finance*, 11th edition, page 120-121.)

There are four steps in determining whether or not you should file so you can obtain your federal income tax refund. Step 1: Calculate an estimate of your tax liability, as shown in Step 10 in Worksheet 20. Step 2: Add up the total amounts withheld for federal income taxes. Step 3: Calculate your refund due or amount owed. Step 4: File for a refund if you are due a refund.

Should-I-File-for-a-Refund Worksheet

Step 1: My estimated tax liability is $_____ (from Step 10 in Worksheet 20)

Step 2: The total amounts withheld for federal taxes is $_____ (from the total of the amounts in column B below)

(A) Income sources	(B) Amounts withheld for federal income taxes
	$
	$
	$
	$
	$
	$
Total	$

Step 3: Calculate your refund due or amount owed:

The total amount withheld (from Step 2)	$_____
Subtotal	$_____
Subtract your estimated tax liability (from Step 1)	$_____
Calculate the refund due you or the amount you owe	$_____

Step 4: File for a refund if you are due a refund.

To obtain your refund, you must file a federal income tax return. If you also have had state and/or city income taxes withheld, you may follow the same step-by-step process to determine if you are owed a refund from your state or city. If so, file appropriate tax forms to claim any refund amounts due from those governments.

WORKSHEET 22—STRATEGIES TO REDUCE MY INCOME TAX LIABILITY

There are several ways to reduce your income tax liability. For each of the strategies below that are of interest to you, identify what one characteristic you like about it, and note which strategies you might follow during your tax-paying life. (Use with *Personal Finance*, 11th edition, pages 124-133.)

Income Tax Reduction Strategies Worksheet

Tax reduction strategy	Note one characteristic I like about the strategy. (*Only comment below if the strategy is of interest to you.*)	Checkmark each strategy I might follow.
Investing with pre-tax income		
Deferring taxes on investment income		
Premium conversion account		
Flexible spending account		
Defined-contribution retirement account		
Individual Retirement Account (IRA)		
Roth IRA		
Coverdell education savings account		
Qualified tuition (Section 529) program		
American Opportunity Tax Credit		
Lifetime Learning Credit		
Government savings bonds		
Municipal bonds		
Earned income credit		
Child/dependent care credit		
Accelerate deductions		
Retirement Savings Contribution Credit		
Take all legal deductions		
Buy and manage a real estate investment		
Other		

WORKSHEET 23—SELECTING A CHECKING ACCOUNT THAT MEETS MY NEEDS

With the low interest rates prevalent today and the high fees that accompany many checking accounts, it is important to choose an account that fits your personal usage patterns. Worksheet 23 provides a way for you to analyze your checking account usage patterns and to estimate the costs associated with various options available to you to ensure that you have chosen the right account. In Step 1 you will identify the ways that you use a checking account. If you currently have a checking account, you can use your past two or three monthly statements to estimate the answers to the questions asked. If you currently do not have a checking account, you can make your best estimate of the answers.

Step 2 provides a way for you to estimate the costs associated with various accounts that are available to you at your current or other financial institutions. Your answers should be based on the usage patterns you identified in Step 1. If you currently have a checking account, you should go back to your account statements over the past two or three months to determine the amounts. You can use the three right columns to record the likely interest and fees associated with other account options. A financial institution that wants your business would be happy to help you estimate these items based on your usage patterns as outlined in Step 1. The goal is to choose an account that has the lowest overall cost given your usage patterns. (Use with *Personal Finance*, 11th edition, pages 144-147.)

Comparing Checking Account Options Worksheet

Step 1—My Checking Account Usage Patterns

How many checks do or will I write per month?   _____

How many ATM transactions do or will I perform each month?   _____

What is the lowest dollar balance I will likely have in my account each month?   _____

What is the highest dollar balance I will likely have in my account each month? _____

What is the average dollar balance I will typically have in my account each month? _____

Will I conduct my checking account on-line?   _____

Will my paycheck be electronically deposited into my checking account?   _____

Step 2—Net Earnings (or Costs) on My Checking Account

	Current Account	Account Option #1	Account Option #2	Account Option #3
Name of financial institution				
Type (name) of account				
Item				
A. Monthly interest or dividends earned				
Fees:				
ATM usage fees (charged by my bank)				
Total per check transaction fees				
Monthly account maintenance fee				
Overdraft fees				
On-line access fees				
Low-balance fees				
Other fees				
B. Total fees				
C. Net earnings or costs (A − B)				

WORKSHEET 24—RECONCILING MY CHECKING ACCOUNT

You should reconcile your checking account each month. Reconciling is the process of comparing your records with those on your monthly account statement. The goals are to make sure that your account balance is accurate, to correct and update your records, and to check the monthly statement for errors the bank may have made. Worksheet 24 provides a form you can use for this reconciliation process.

In Step 1, record the balance shown on your account statement. In Step 2, total all outstanding deposits. In Step 3, subtract the Step 2 result from the Step 1 figure. In Step 4, total all outstanding checks or debits to your account. In Step 5, subtract the Step 4 result from Step 3 figure. The result is the up-to-date statement balance.

In Step 6, record the current balance in your checkbook register. In Step 7, total all credits to your account that you had not previously recorded. In Step 8, record any interest payments into your account as shown on your monthly account statement. In Step 9, add the results from Steps 6, 7, and 8. In Step 10, total any debits from your account that were not previously recorded in your checkbook register. In Step 11, record any fees charged to your account as indicated on your monthly account statement. In Step 12, subtract the results for Step 10 and Step 11 from Step 9. The result is your up-to-date check register balance. The results for Step 5 and Step 12 should agree. If they do not, you will need to determine where an error may have occurred. An interactive calculator that performs this same procedure can be found on the Garman/Forgue companion website. (Use with *Personal Finance*, 11th edition, page 150.)

Checking Account Reconciliation Worksheet for Month/Year _____

Worksheet	Reconciling My Checking Account	
	Checking Account Reconciliation for (Month/Year?)	
Step A: Updating Your Records		Step B: Updating the Bank's Records
	Amount		**Amount**
#1 Balance Shown in Check Register	$	#1 Balance Shown on Statement	$
List Deposits/Credits Not Recorded in Check Register		List Outstanding Deposits (by date)	
	$		$
	$		$
	$		$
	$		$
	$		$
#2 Add Total Deposits/Credits Not Recorded	$	#2 Add Total Outstanding Deposits	$
		Adjusted Statement Balance	$
List Checks/Debits Not Recorded in Check Register			
	$	List Outstanding Checks/ Debits (by Check #)	
	$		$
	$		$
	$		$
	$		$
	$		$
	$		$
	$		$
	$		$

#3 Subtract Total Checks/Debits Not Recorded	$		$
			$
#4 Subtract Account Fees	$		$
			$
#5 Add Interest Earned	$		$
			$
#6 Up-to-Date Check Register Balance			$
			$
		#3 Total Outstanding Checks	$
		#4 Up-to-date Statement Balance	$ -
STEP C: Compare adjusted checkbook register balance and adjusted bank statement balance. If the two balances do not match, identify where the error occurred.			

WORKSHEET 25—THE EFFECT OF TAKING ON ADDITIONAL DEBT ON MY FINANCIAL RATIOS

Three key financial ratios can provide additional insights into the affordability of taking on additional debt. Worksheet 25 builds upon Worksheet 12 to provide those insights. (Use with *Personal Finance*, 11th edition, pages 173-178.)

The **debt service-to-income ratio** compares your total annual debt payments (including home mortgage debt) with your gross annual income. A debt service-to-income ratio in excess of 0.36 indicates that you are carrying too much debt. What if you were to take on more debt? How would your debt service-to-income ratio change from what you calculated in Worksheet 12?

The **debt payments-to-disposable income ratio** compares your monthly nonmortgage debt payments to your monthly disposable income. A debt service-to-disposable income ratio of 0.15 or more indicates that you are carrying too much nonmortgage debt. What if you were to take on more debt? How would your debt payments-to-disposable income ratio change from what you calculated in Worksheet 12?

The **debt-to-equity ratio** uses the **equity** in a person's assets (the amount by which the value of those assets exceeds debts), excluding the value of a primary residence and the amount owed on first mortgage on that home. This ratio recognizes that mortgage debt does not get people into trouble. In fact, mortgage debt is backed up by excellent collateral—one's own home. An interactive calculator that performs these same procedures can be found on the Garman/Forgue companion website.

The Effect of Taking on Additional Debt on My Financial Ratios Worksheet

Debt service-to-income ratio:

(A) Current annual debt repayments	(B) Gross income	(C) Current debt service-to-income ratio(A divided by B)	(D) New annual debt repayments	(E) **New debt service-to-income ratio** (D divided by B)

Debt payments-to-disposable income ratio:

(A) Current monthly nonmortgage debt payments	(B) Disposable income	(C) **Current debt payments-to-disposable income ratio** (A divided by B)	(D) New monthly nonmortgage debt repayments	(E) **New debt payments-to-disposable income ratio** (D divided by E)

Debt-to-equity ratio:

(A) Total debts excluding mortgage debt	(B) Current assets excluding the value of a home	(C) **Current debt-to-equity ratio** (A divided by B)	(D) New total debts excluding mortgage debt	(E) New current assets excluding the value of a home	(F) **New debt-to-equity ratio** (D divided by E)

WORKSHEET 26—MY INSTALLMENT LOAN INVENTORY

Have you taken out a loan for a vehicle, vacation, or other purpose? How many loans other than student loans (see Worksheet 27) do you have outstanding? Worksheet 26 provides a handy way to list all your loans. It gives you a clear picture of your outstanding installment debts. The information needed to complete this inventory can be found in your monthly statements or original loan contracts. (Use with *Personal Finance*, 11th edition, pages 173-178.)

My Installment Loan Inventory

	Name and address of lender	Reason for the loan	Original loan amount	Monthly payment	Due date	Payoff date
Loan #1						
Loan #2						
Loan #3						
Loan #4						
Loan #5						
Loan #6						

WORKSHEET 27—MY STUDENT LOAN INVENTORY

Do you have any outstanding student loans? Worksheet 27 provides a handy way to list each of your student loans along with relevant information about the source of the funds, lender, amount owed, loan costs, etc. When you graduate, you may be able to consolidate all your loans into one to receive a lower APR. This worksheet will help you get started in that process. (Use with *Personal Finance*, 11th edition, pages 173-178.)

My Student Loan Inventory

Loan feature	Loan #1	Loan #2	Loan #3	Loan #4
Program through which loan was obtained				
Interest deferred? (yes/no)				
If interest is deferred, when must payments begin?				
Source/lender				
Current APR				
Current loan balance				
Maximum number of years to repay				
Approximate monthly payment (see Table 7.3 in text or Worksheet 25)				

WORKSHEET 28—MY CREDIT CARD ACCOUNTS INVENTORY

The typical American with a credit card has an average of seven open accounts. Accounts stay open even if not used for several years. Worksheet 26 provides a quick way for you to list your accounts and the information needed to contact the lender in case the card is lost or stolen, there is an error on your monthly statement, or if you change your address. These numbers can be found on your monthly statement or the website for the issuing financial institution. (Use with *Personal Finance*, 11th edition, pages 198-205.)

My Credit Card Accounts Inventory

	Name of card	Issuing financial institution	Account number	APFs	Usual due date	Phone number to notify if lost or stolen	Phone number to notify of a billing error
Card #1							
Card #2							
Card #3							
Card #4							
Card #5							
Card #6							
Card #7							
Card #8							
Card #9							
Card #10							

WORKSHEET 29—COMPARING MY CREDIT CARD OPTIONS

All credit card offers are not alike. In addition to the obvious differences in APRs and annual fees, there are a number of other features of cards that distinguish among appropriate and inappropriate offers given your likely usage patterns. Worksheet 25 allows you to summarize several offers side-by-side for easy analysis and selection. (Use with *Personal Finance*, 11th edition, pages 198-205.)

Comparing My Credit Card Options Worksheet

Card feature	Card #1	Card #2	Card #3
Type of card (VISA, MC, AMEX, etc.)			
Company/bank offering the card			

Introductory APRs
  Purchases
  Cash advances
  Balance transfers			

Subsequent APRs
  Purchases
  Cash advances
  Balance transfers			

Default APRs
  Purchases
  Cash advances
  Balance transfers			

If APRs are variable, what base rate is used?			

If APRs are variable, what percentage is added to the base rate to arrive at the APR?
  Purchases
  Cash advances
  Balance transfers			

Annual fee			
Method of computing the balance			
Grace period for purchases			
Minimum finance charge			

Transaction fees
  Purchases
  Cash advances
  Balance transfers			

Additional fees
  Over-the-limit fee
  Late payment fee
  Bounced check fee			

WORKSHEET 30—MONTHLY INSTALLMENT LOAN PAYMENT CALCULATOR

Whenever you apply for an installment loan, you will be faced with a number of options regarding the amount to borrow, the APR of the loan, and the time period of the loan. Changes in any one of these factors will result in a different monthly payment on the loan for principal and interest. This worksheet can be used in conjunction with Table 7.1 on page xxx in your text to calculate the monthly payment for loans with differing factors. An interactive calculator that performs this same procedure can be found on the Garman/Forgue companion website. (Use with *Personal Finance*, 11th edition, pages 212-216.)

Monthly Installment Loan Payment Calculation Worksheet

(A) Loan	(B) Time period of the loan in months	(C) APR of the loan	(D) Factor from Table 7.3 that corresponds with (B) and (C)	(E) Amount borrowed	(F) Amount borrowed (E) divided by 1,000	(G) Monthly payment (D x F)
#1						
#2						
#3						
#4						
#5						
#6						

WORKSHEET 31—MY TOP PRIORITY MOTOR VEHICLE FEATURES

The number of options available on vehicles today is almost limitless. Before you begin shopping for a vehicle, it is wise to think through the options that you desire and assign a priority level to each. Worksheet 29 provides a mechanism for this task by listing many common features so you can use a checkmark to assign each to one of three priority levels: 1 for essential features; 2 for highly desirable features; and 3 for "nice to have" features. Features that are not desired can be left unchecked. Blank rows are included for you to include additional features that you might desire. (Use with *Personal Finance*, 11th edition, pages 224-225.)

My Vehicle Features Worksheet

Vehicle feature	Priority Level		
	1	2	3
Adjustable steering column			
Side-impact air bags			
Air conditioning			
Satellite radio			
Four-wheel anti-lock brakes			
Automatic transmission			
Central power locking system			
CD player/changer			
Cruise control			
All-wheel drive			
4-wheel drive			
Power windows			
Rear-window defroster			
Sun/moon roof			
Theft-deterrence system			
Advanced sound system			
DVD player			
Power adjustable seating			
Heated seats			
Remote keyless entry			
Removable rear seating			
Luggage rack			
GPS system			
Towing package			
High gas mileage rating			
Daytime running lights			
Power mirrors			
Integrated child seat			

WORKSHEET 32—COMPARING VEHICLE PURCHASE CONTRACTS

Buying a vehicle can be a very complicated process. There are so many variables that many people simply focus on one or two aspects such as the monthly payment or the trade-in value. This can be a recipe for a bad deal because the profit that a dealer might give up on one aspect can be more than made up for on another. Worksheet 30 provides a handy place to record all of the terms for several purchase contracts from three dealers. The worksheet allows you to see the full picture and make accurate comparisons. (Use with *Personal Finance*, 11th edition, pages 228-238.)

Vehicle Purchase Contract Worksheet

Contract provision	Dealer #1	Dealer #2	Dealer #3
Vehicle sticker price			
Vehicle invoice price (estimated)			
Dealer offer price			
Trade-in value offered by dealer			
APR by source of financing			
• Manufacturer			
• Dealer			
• Your own arrangement			
Is there a rebate? (if so, complete Worksheet 32)			
Down payment			
Amount borrowed			
Length of loan			
Monthly payment			
Warranty provisions			
• Miles/years			
• Coverage (drive train, bumper to bumper?)			
Service contract provisions			
• Miles			
• Coverage (drive train, bumper to bumper?)			
• Cost			
Cost of dealer option package			
Cost of gap insurance			

WORKSHEET 33—SHOULD I LEASE OR BUY A VEHICLE?

The worksheet below can be used to compare leasing and borrowing to buy a vehicle. Remember that the cost of credit is the finance charge—the extra that you pay because you borrowed. In the example below, the finance charge on the loan is $1,950. Your lender will be able to tell you the finance charge on any vehicle loan offer you are considering.

Leases also carry costs, but they are hidden in the contract, and some remain unknown until the end of the lease period. These items, which are indicated by an asterisk (*) below, are negotiable and are defined in the text. Ask the dealer for the amount of each of these costs. Then complete the worksheet and compare the dollar cost of leasing with the finance charge on a loan for the same time period.

In Step 1, total all the monthly lease payments as outlined in the contract. In Step 2, record other charges for which you will be responsible (note that you cover the residual value of the vehicle by returning or buying the vehicle at the end of the lease period). Step 3 is the total for Steps 2 and 3. In Step 4, record the adjusted capitalized cost (capitalized cost less items such as a trade-in and down payment) as indicated in your contract. Step 5 is the result of subtracting Step 4 from Step 1. In Step 6, record the finance charge on the loan you would arrange to buy the vehicle instead of leasing. The lower of items Step 5 and Step 6 is the better arrangement. In the example, the $1,950 finance charge is lower than the $2,600 additional cost of leasing. This means that you should borrow to buy the vehicle rather than obtain it with a lease.

To make the comparison accurately, you must know the underlying price of the car if you were purchasing it. Often you are not told this value with a lease arrangement, so you must negotiate a price for the vehicle before mentioning the lease option. An interactive calculator that performs this same procedure can be found on the Garman/Forgue companion website. (Use with *Personal Finance*, 11th edition, pages 229-232.)

Vehicle Lease versus Buy Worksheet

Step	(A) Example	(B) Your figures
1. Total monthly lease payments (36 payments of $275, for example)	$ 13,500	
2. Plus acquisition fee* (if any) • Plus disposition charge* (if any) • Plus estimate of excess mileage charges* (if any) • Plus projected residual value of the vehicle	+ 300 + 300 + 00 + 4,500	
3. Amount for which you are responsible under the lease (#1 plus #2)	$ 18,600	
4. Adjusted capitalized cost*—the capitalized cost* after taking capitalized cost reductions*	– 16,000	
5. Dollar cost of leasing (#3 minus #4)	$ 2,600	
6. Finance charge for loan you arrange to purchase rather than lease the vehicle	$ 1,950	

WORKSHEET 34—SHOULD I TAKE A NEW VEHICLE REBATE OR LOW-RATE FINANCING OFFER?

Ads for new vehicles often offer either a low APR loan or a cash rebate of $1,000 to $3,000 (or more) off the price of the car. Which alternative is better when you can arrange your own financing? You can't simply compare the dealer APR to the APR that you arranged on your own.

To compare the two APRs accurately, you must add the opportunity cost of the foregone rebate to the finance charge of the dealer financing. The worksheet below provides an example (Column A) of this process for an offer with a $3,000 rebate versus a loan of $20,000 with a 2.9% APR for three years with a $907 finance charge.

In Step 1, record the dollar value of the rebate offered. In Step 2, add the rebate amount to the finance charge that would be required by the loan obtained via the low-rate financing offer. Step 3 requires that you use the n-ratio formula (7.2) in your text to recalculate the low-rate finance APR. In Step 4, record the APR for the best loan you can arrange on your own through your bank or credit union. The lower of the values obtained in Steps 3 and 4 is the better deal. In the example below, the financing that you could arrange on your own is more attractive. In fact, any loan that carries an APR lower than 11.99 percent compares favorably with the dealer-arranged 6.5 percent financing in this case. An interactive calculator that performs this same procedure can be found on the Garman/Forgue companion website. (Use with *Personal Finance*, 11th edition, page 230.)

New Vehicle Rebate or Low-rate Financing Offer Worksheet

Step	(A) Example	(B) Your Figures
1. Determine the dollar amount of the rebate.	$ 3,000	
2. Add the rebate amount to the finance charge for the dealer financing (dollar cost of credit).	+ 907 = $ 3,907	
3. Use the n-ratio APR formula from Chapter 7 (Equation 7.2 on page 215) to calculate an adjusted APR for the dealer financing.	12%	
4. Write in the APR that you arranged on your own.	6.5%	

WORKSHEET 35—DECISION MAKING WORKSHEET FOR A MAJOR PRODUCT PURCHASE

Making a major purchase decision can be a difficult task. It sometimes helps to puts some numbers to the decision. For example, price might represent 50 percent of the importance you place on the various criteria. Worksheet 33 allows you to calculate a total weighted score for up to three different models of a product. In Step 1 (Column A), assign weights to the criteria. Then in Step 2, give each model a score for each criteria on a 10-point scale (Columns B, D, and F). For Step 3, calculate the weighted scores for each of the criteria for each model (Columns C, E, G). Finally, in Step 4, total up the weighted scores for each model. The one with the highest total weighted score will stand above the others on the criteria you have chosen. An interactive calculator that performs this same procedure can be found on the Garman/Forgue companion website. (Use with *Personal Finance*, 11th edition, pages 237-238.)

Decision Making Worksheet for a Major Product Purchase

Criteria	(A) **Step 1** Decision Weight	(B) **(Step 2)** Score 1*	(C) **(Step 3)** Weighted Score 1 (A x B)	(D) **(Step 2)** Score 2*	(E) **(Step 3)** Weighted Score 2 (A x D)	(F) **(Step 2)** Score 3*	(G) **(Step 3)** Weighted Score 3 (A x F)
		Model 1		**Model 2**		**Model 3**	
Price							
Durability							
Features							
Warranty							
Styling							
Other							
Other							
(Step 4) **TOTAL**							

*Using a 10-point scale where 10 is the highest score.

WORKSHEET 36—SAMPLE PRODUCT OR SERVICE COMPLAINT LETTER

The final step in wise buying is to evaluate your decision. Sometimes this evaluation results in a desire to complain or seek redress for some deficiency in the product or service you purchased. A simple "I don't like …." is not usually sufficient to correct the problem. Instead, a letter containing all the specifics of the problem and the remedy desired is likely to get action. Worksheet 34 provides a sample letter you can use whenever seeking redress of a deficient product or service. (Use with *Personal Finance*, 11th edition, pages 240-241.)

Sample Product or Service Complaint Letter

(Your address)
(Your city, state, zip code)

(Date)

(Name of contact person)
(Title)
(Company name)
(Street address)
(City, state, zip code)

Dear (contact person):

On (date), I purchased (or had repaired) a (name of the product with the serial or model number or service performed). I made this purchase at (location, date, and other important details of the transaction).

Unfortunately, your product (or service) has not been satisfactory because (state the problem).

Therefore, to resolve the problem, I request that you (state the specific action you want).

Enclosed are copies (copies, *not* originals) of my records (receipts, guarantees, warranties, cancelled checks, contracts, model and serial numbers, and any other documents).

I look forward to your reply and a resolution to my problem and will wait (set a time limit) before seeking third-party assistance.

Please contact me at the above address or by phone (home or office numbers with area codes).

Sincerely,

(Your name)

(Your account number)

WORKSHEET 37—SHOULD I RENT OR BUY HOUSING?

This worksheet can be used to help you estimate whether you would be better off renting housing or buying over the first year of a home purchase. An interactive calculator that performs this same procedure can be found on the Garman/Forgue companion website. (Use with *Personal Finance*, 11th edition, pages 249-253.)

Should I Rent or Buy Housing Worksheet

	(A) Example amounts (from text)		(B) Your figures	
	Rent	**Buy**	**Rent**	**Buy**
Step 1—Annual cash flow considerations				
Annual rent ($1000/month) or mortgage payments ($863.35/month)*	$12,000	$ 10,360		
Property and liability insurance	360	725		
Private mortgage insurance	N/A	0	N/A	
Real estate taxes	0	3,000		
Maintenance	0	600		
Other housing fees	0	1,800		
Less interest earned on funds not used for down payment (at 2%)	– 720	N/A		N/A
Net cash-flow cost for the year	$11,640	$ 16,485		
Step 2—Tax and appreciation considerations				
Less principal[†] repaid on the mortgage loan	N/A	– 1,768	N/A	
Plus tax on interest earned on funds not used for down payment (25% marginal tax bracket)	270	N/A		N/A
Less tax savings due to deductibility of mortgage interest[‡] (25% marginal tax bracket)	N/A	– 2,148	N/A	
Less tax savings due to deductibility of real estate property taxes (25% marginal tax bracket)	N/A	– 750	N/A	
Less appreciation on the dwelling (2% annual rate)	N/A	– 3,600	N/A	
Step 3—Net cost for the year (Step 1 plus or minus Step 2)	$11,550	$8,219		

*Calculated using Table 9.4 in your text.
[†]Calculated according to the method illustrated in Table 9.2 in your text.
[‡]Mortgage interest tax savings equal total mortgage payments minus principal repaid multiplied by the marginal tax rate.

WORKSHEET 38—INCOME NEEDED TO QUALIFY FOR A MORTGAGE CALCULATOR

Lenders will use one or both of the front-end and back-end ratios to determine the amount of income you will need to qualify for a specified loan amount. You can use the table on page xxx in the text for a rough estimate. Or you can use the worksheet below. Use Table 9.4 to calculate the monthly payment on the loan for principal and interest. Then multiple the purchase price by 1.5% to determine the additional amount needed per month for real estate taxes and homeowner's insurance. To determine the income needed divide the total monthly payment by the front-end ratio desired by your lender. (Use with *Personal Finance*, 11th edition, pages 261-263.)

| | **Income Needed to Qualify for a Mortgage*** | |
	Example from Text	**Insert Your Figures**
Purchase price of the home	$180,000	
Percentage down payment	20%	
Down payment	$36,000	
Dollar amount borrowed	$144,000	
Length of the mortgage Period in months	360	
Interest rate on the mortgage	6%	
Monthly payment on the loan (*P* and *I*)	$863.35	
Total monthly payment including taxes and insurance (*T* and *I*)*	$1,088.35	
Front-end ratio required**	0.28	
Income required	$46,643	

*Taxes and insurance are assumed at 1.5% of the home's value.
**Consult your prospective lenders for their requirements.

WORKSHEET 39—MORTGAGE SHOPPING WORKSHEET

There are several different types of mortgages from which you may choose and many different sources of mortgage loans. You will want to compare your options in a systematic way and have all of the information in a handy, accessible format. It allows you to list four different loan options. Simply add columns should you have more options from which to choose. Worksheet 39 can help you do so. (Use with *Personal Finance*, 11th edition, pages 265-276.)

Consideration	Loan Option 1	Loan Option 2	Loan Option 3	Loan Option 4
DESCRIPTIVE INFORMATION				
Type of mortgage (fixed-rate, adjustable-rate, graduated payment, etc.)?				
Minimum required down payment?				
Loan term in years?				
Quoted initial interest rate?				
Initial APR?				
Number of points?				
Monthly PMI premiums (if required)?				
Mortgage lock-in available?				
Estimated monthly payment for principal and interest?				
Total monthly payment for PITI and PMI?				
For adjustable-rate and graduated payment loans				
Index used for making adjustments (LIBOR?				

Prime Rate?)?				
Margin added to index?				
Frequency of possible Rate change?				
Maximum possible rate after 1 year?				
Maximum new monthly payment after 1 year?				
Annual interest rate cap?				
Maximum possible interest rate over life of loan?				
Maximum possible payment over life of loan?				
Up-front Fees				
Application, origination, loan processing fees?				
Mortgage broker fees?				
Credit report fees?				
Rate lock-in fee?				
Title search/insurance fee?				
Transfer tax/deed filing fee?				
Prepaid PMI fee?				
Appraisal fee?				
Other fees?				

WORKSHEET 40—ESTIMATING HOME BUYING AND CLOSING COSTS

Buying a home requires that you carefully consider all of the costs associated with the mortgage used to make the purchase. These costs include all payments made at the closing and then all of the monthly expenditures, as well. Worksheet 38 provides a way for you to record the costs for your mortgage in a handy summary form. Most of the information can be obtained from the "good faith estimate" that lenders must provide when you apply for a mortgage loan. (Use with *Personal Finance*, 11th edition, pages 265-276.)

Estimating Home Buying and Closing Costs Worksheet

Home buying costs	At closing	Monthly
Down payment		
Points		
Loan application fee		
Principal and interest[†]		
Property taxes	*	
Homeowner's insurance	**	
Mortgage insurance		
Loan origination fee		
Title search		
Title insurance (to protect lender)		
Title insurance (to protect buyer)		
Attorney's fee		
Credit reports		
Recording fees		
Appraisal fee		
Termite and radon inspection fees		
Survey fee		
Notary fee		
Subtotal		
Less amount owed by seller	*	
Subtotal		
Warranty insurance (optional)		
TOTAL		

*Would be received from seller, who legally owes these taxes, and then deposited in escrow account.
**Would be paid to escrow account.
[†]Calculated using Table 9.4 in your text or Worksheet 41.

WORSHEET 41—MONTHLY MORTGAGE PAYMENT CALCULATOR

Whenever you apply for a mortgage loan you will be faced with a number of options regarding the amount to borrow, the APR of the loan, and the time period of the loan. Changes in any one of these factors will result in a different monthly payment for principal and interest. This worksheet can be used in conjunction with Table 9.4 on page xxx in your text to calculate the monthly payment for mortgage loans with differing factors. An interactive calculator that performs this same procedure can be found on the Garman/Forgue companion website. (Use with *Personal Finance*, 11th edition, pages 267-271.)

Monthly Mortgage Loan Payment Calculation Worksheet

(A) Mortgage loan	(B) Time period of the loan in years	(C) Interest rate of the loan	(D) Factor from Table 9.4 that corresponds with (B) and (C)	(E) Amount borrowed	(F) Amount borrowed (E) divided by 1,000	(G) Monthly payment (D x F)
#1						
#2						
#3						
#4						
#5						
#6						

WORKSHEET 42—SHOULD I REFINANCE MY MORTGAGE?

In times of low interest rates, many people wonder whether they should take out a new loan to pay off their current high rate mortgage to take advantage of the lower current rates. Such an arrangement is referred to as a mortgage refinancing.

Worksheet 42 provides a way for you to decide whether it is financial advantageous to refinance a mortgage. Note that the worksheet is only applicable if you are borrowing only the current outstanding loan balance for the same number of years as are remaining on the current loan.

In Step 1, record the current monthly payment on your mortgage for principal and interest only (not taxes and insurance). In Step 2, record the monthly payment for principal and interest only (not taxes and insurance) on the new mortgage. In Step 3, subtract Step 2 from Step 1 and multiply by 12 to obtain your annual mortgage payment reduction. In Step 4, estimate the number of years you remain living in the home. In Step 5, determine how much you could save if you placed the monthly mortgage payment reduction into a savings account. You will have to estimate the interest rate after taxes that could be achieved on this account. In Step 6, record any prepayment penalties for paying off your current loan early. In Step 7, record the total of all up-front costs for the new loan including points and other fees. In Step 8, determine the future value if you would instead invest the up-front costs into a savings account rather than use them to refinance. Again, you will have to estimate the interest rate after taxes that could be achieved on this account.

In Step 9, subtract the results of Step 5 from the results of Step 8. The result is an estimate of the net savings from refinancing the mortgage.

In the example, it would appear that refinancing would benefit the owner. An interactive calculator that performs this same procedure can be found on the Garman/Forgue companion website. (Use with *Personal Finance*, 11th edition, page 275.)

Should I Refinance My Mortgage? Worksheet

(A) Step	(B) Example	(C) Your figures
1. Current monthly payment	$ 908	
2. New monthly payment	827	
3. Monthly savings (Step 1 minus Step 2 x 12)	81	
4. Additional years you expect to live in the house	4	
5. Future value of an account balance after 4 years if the monthly savings were invested at 3% after taxes (using Appendix A.3)	4,175	
6. Prepayment penalty on current loan (if any)	0	
7. Points and fees for new loan	2,844	
8. Future value of an account balance after 4 years if the prepayment penalty and closing costs ($4,200) had been invested instead at 3% after taxes (using Appendix A.1)	3,201	
9. Net saving after 48 months (Step 5 minus Step 8)	$ 974	

SECTION THREE

INCOME AND ASSET PROTECTION

This section of your workbook focuses on efforts to protect your property and income from loss. Each worksheet will allow you to think through a decision or perform calculations related to a specific area of personal financial management in a way that has direct benefit to you. Worksheets marked with an asterisk can be found on the Garman/Forgue companion website at www.cengagebrain.com.

WORKSHEET 43—MY INSURANCE INVENTORY

As your financial life get more complicated and you own more possessions, your need for insurance protection also increases. Most Americans are covered by five major types of insurance: life, health, automobile, homeowner's, and disability income. The details of each of these protections are contained in the actual insurance policies. It helps to have the basic information about all your policies in one place for handy reference. Worksheet 43 provides an insurance inventory you can use for this purpose. (Use with *Personal Finance*, 11th edition, pages 288-370.)

My Insurance Inventory Worksheets

Insurance Inventory Worksheet for _____

Do you have life insurance? If so, complete the following for each policy.	Policy limits (face amount)	Annual premium	Beneficiary	Term or cash value policy?	If cash value, what is the current cash value?
Company: Policy #: Agent: Contact Info:					
Company: Policy #: Agent: Contact Info:					
Company: Policy #: Agent: Contact Info:					

Are you covered by any health care plans? If so, complete the following.	Is it an HMO? What is its name?	Is it traditional insurance? What company?	If insurance, what is the aggregate limit?	Does an employer pay all or a portion of the premium?	Do you or a parent or guardian pay part of the premium? If so, how much?
Company: Policy or plan #: Agent: Contact info:					
Company: Policy or plan #: Agent: Contact info:					

Do you have disability income insurance? If so complete the following.	Amount of monthly premium?	Annual premium?	Waiting period?	Maximum benefit period?
Company: Policy #: Agent: Contact info:				
Company: Policy #: Agent: Contact info:				

Do you have automobile insurance on the vehicles you drive? Describe the vehicle covered including the VIN number. Also complete the following.	What are the liability limits? ($/$/$)	Collision deductible? (N/A if no collision)	"Other than collision" deductible?	Under- or uninsured motorist limits?	Medical payment (PIP) limits?
Description and VIN: Company: Policy or plan #: Agent: Contact info:					
Description and VIN: Company: Policy or plan #: Agent: Contact info:					

Are you covered by homeowner's or renter's insurance? Which form? (HO-1, HO-2, etc.) If so, complete the following.	Limit on dwelling?	Limit on personal property?	Personal liability limit?	Deductible amount?	Annual premium?
Form: Company: Policy #: Agent: Contact info:					

WORKSHEET 44—MY HOME INVENTORY

Making an inventory of, and placing a value on, all the contents of your home are time-consuming efforts but important tasks. Should some or all of these assets be stolen or lost in a fire or natural disaster, providing a copy of a home inventory worksheet to your insurance company can greatly aid the process of filing a claim. An interactive calculator that calculates actual cash values can be found on the Garman/Forgue companion website. Worksheet 44 provides a form you can use for this purpose. (Use with *Personal Finance*, 11th edition, pages 288-289, 296-300.)

Home Inventory Worksheet

Date inventory prepared: _____

Items	Item description	Date purchased	Purchase price	Actual cash value	Replace-ment cost
Living room:					
			$	$	$
			$	$	$
			$	$	$
			$	$	$
Dining room:					
			$	$	$
			$	$	$
			$	$	$
			$	$	$
Kitchen:					
			$	$	$
			$	$	$
			$	$	$
Bedrooms:					
			$	$	$
			$	$	$
			$	$	$
Hallways:					
			$	$	$
			$	$	$
Home office:					
			$	$	$
			$	$	$
Bathroom:					
			$	$	$
			$	$	$
Garage, attic, basement, and storage:					
			$	$	$
			$	$	$
Other items:					
			$	$	$
			$	$	$

WORKSHEET 45—MY COMPARISON OF AUTO INSURANCE PROVIDERS

The premium required for automobile insurance varies considerably from company to company and from driver to driver. Automobile insurance definitely is one of those areas where it pays to shop around. Worksheet 45 provides a mechanism for recording automobile insurance premium quotations from insurers. (Use with *Personal Finance*, 11th edition, pages 302-307.)

Auto Insurance Comparison Worksheet

Coverage type	Coverage limits or amount of deductible	Company 1 premium for each component	Company 2 premium for each component	Company 3 premium for each component
A. Liability insurance Bodily injury	$_____ /$_____	$_____	$_____	$_____
Property damage	$_____ /$_____	$_____	$_____	$_____
B. Medical payment/personal injury protection Medical payments	$_____ /$_____	$_____	$_____	$_____
PIP (no-fault states)	$_____ /$_____	$_____	$_____	$_____
C. Uninsured/underinsured motorist protection Uninsured motorist	$_____ /$_____	$_____	$_____	$_____
Underinsured motorist	$_____ /$_____	$_____	$_____	$_____
D. Physical damage protection Collision coverage	$_____ deductible	$_____	$_____	$_____
Comprehensive	$_____ deductible	$_____	$_____	$_____
Total Premium		$_____	$_____	$_____
Plus Surcharges		$_____	$_____	$_____
Less Discounts		$_____	$_____	$_____
Final Total Premium		$_____	$_____	$_____

WORKSHEET 46—DETERMINING MY DISABILITY INCOME INSURANCE NEEDS

Disability income insurance is one of the most overlooked forms of insurance yet is especially vital for young workers who have not established retirement funds or Social Security earnings histories that can provide support in times of disability. Worksheet 46 can be used to estimate the monthly dollar amount of your disability income insurance needs.

The determination of disability insurance needs begins with your current monthly after-tax income. From this figure, subtract the amounts you would receive from Social Security disability and other sources of disability income. The resulting figure would provide an estimate of extra coverage needed. You should also consult with your employer to determine the provisions of any disability income insurance protection that is provided as an employee benefit. An interactive calculator that performs this same procedure can be found on the Garman/Forgue companion website. (Use with *Personal Finance*, 11th edition, pages 333-337.)

Disability Income Insurance Needs Worksheet

	Example	Your Figures
1. Current monthly after-tax income	$2,100	$_____
Minus previous established disability income protections		$_____
2. Estimated monthly Social Security benefits (See Appendix B or use the Benefits Estimator on the Social Security Administration website—www.ssa.gov)	–$750	$_____
3. Monthly benefit from employer-provided disability insurance	–$600	$_____
4. Monthly benefit from private disability insurance		$_____
5. Monthly benefit from other government disability insurance		$_____
6. Reduction of monthly life insurance premiums due to waiver of premiums on these policies		$_____
7. Total currently established disability income protections (Total of Step 2 through Step 6)	$1,350	$_____
8. Estimated monthly disability income insurance needs. (Step 1 minus Step 7)	$ 750	$_____

WORKSHEET 47—DETERMINING MY LIFE INSURANCE NEEDS

Life insurance needs vary considerably over the life cycle. They are low for single adults, peak when becoming a parent for the first time and then slowly decline as children grow up. Thus, it is important to recalculate your needs every 3 to 5 years or when a major life transition occurs such as marriage, parenthood, divorce, death of a spouse or child, or major change in your level of income.

Worksheet 47 can be used to calculate your life insurance needs using the needs approach outlined in your textbook. An interactive calculator that performs this same procedure can be found on the Garman/Forgue companion website. (Use with *Personal Finance*, 11th edition, pages 346-351.)

My Life Insurance Needs Worksheet

Factors affecting need		Example	Your figures
1. Income-replacement needs Multiply 75 percent of annual income* by the interest factor from Appendix A.4 that corresponds with the number of years that the income is to be replaced and the assumed after-tax, after-inflation rate of return. ($36,000 x 17.292 for 30 years at a 4% rate of return)	$	705,614	$_____
2. Final-expense needs Includes funeral, burial, travel, and other items of expense just prior to and after death.	+	12,000	+_____
3. Readjustment-period needs To cover employment interruptions and possible education expenses for surviving spouse and dependents.	+	19,000	+_____
4. Debt-repayment needs Provides repayment of short-term and installment debt, including credit cards and personal loans.	+	10,000	+_____
5. College-expense needs To provide a fund to help meet college expenses of dependents.	+	75,000	+_____
6. Other special needs	+	0	+_____
7. Subtotal (combined effects of items 1–6)	$	821,614	+_____
8. Government benefits Present value of Social Security survivor's benefits and other benefits. Multiply monthly benefit estimate by 12 and use Appendix A.4 for the number of years that benefits will be received and the same interest rate that was used in Item 1. ($2,725 x 12 x 11.118 for 15 years of benefits and a 4% rate of return)	–	363,558	–_____
9. Current insurance assets	–	98,000	–_____
10. Life insurance needed	$	360,056	_____

*Seventy-five percent is used because about 25 percent of income is used for personal needs.

WORKSHEET 48—LAYERING TERM INSURANCE POLICIES

Trying to meet one's life insurance needs with just one or two life insurance policies is not the best method of obtaining protection over the life cycle. This is because life insurance needs fluctuate over one's lifetime. The bulk of this need can be met by layering term insurance policies so that coverage grows and then automatically decreases as needs change.

Worksheet 48 can be used to set up your term insurance layers. The worksheet also provides an example you can use as a model. The example assumes that the person is age 25 when a first child is born and age 30 when a last child is born. In this example, the person buys several level premium term policies near the birth of the first child with the policies having differing time periods. Then the person buys another policy when the last child is born and another as the first child gets close to college age. Then as the children go out on their own, some of the earliest policies expire thereby reducing the overall amount of insurance as needs decline. One benefit of layering is affordability. Based on premium rates for healthy, non-smokers the cost for the illustrated plan would never be more than approximately $50 per month. (Use with *Personal Finance*, 11th edition, page 367.)

Term Insurance Layering Worksheet

Example						
Age	**Buy**			**Policies in force at that age**	**Total coverage at that age**	**Monthly premium required**
	Policy	**Face amount**	**Years in force**			
25	#1 #2 #3	$100,000 $150,000 $200,000	30 years 25 years 20 years	#1, #2, #3	$450,000	$38
30	#4	$150,000	25 years	#1, #2, #3, #4	$600,000	$48
35				#1, #2, #3, #4	$600,000	$54
40	#5	$50,000	20 years	#1, #2, #3, #4, #5	$650,000	$60
45				#1, #2, #4, #5	$450,000	$58
50				#1, #4, #5	$300,000	$50
55				#5	$50,000	$20
60				None	$0	$0
Your Plan						
25						
30						
35						
40						
45						
50						
55						
60						

SECTION FOUR

INVESTMENTS

This section of your workbook focuses on investing. Each worksheet will allow you to think through a decision or perform calculations related to a specific area of personal financial management in a way that has direct benefit to you. Worksheets marked with an asterisk can be found on the Garman/Forgue companion website at www.cengagebrain.com.

WORKSHEET 49—MY READINESS-TO-INVEST CHECKLIST

Before you embark on an investment program, make sure you are ready. Give yourself a "readiness grade" of an A, B, C, D, or F for each of the following prerequisites to investing if they are accomplished. Make note of things you can do to improve your readiness to invest and set dates for completion. And begin investing as soon as you can! (Use with *Personal Finance*, 11th edition, pages 380-382.)

Readiness-to-Invest Worksheet

Prerequisite to investing	Your current readiness grade	Things I will do to improve my readiness to invest	Expected completion date
Balance your budget			
Continue a savings plan			
Establish sufficient credit card maximum limits			
Carry adequate insurance to protect against major catastrophes			
Establish investment goals			
Other prerequisite			

WORKSHEET 50—MY INVESTMENT PHILOSOPHY

Before embarking on an investment plan, you need to understand your own approach to investing. Your ability to handle investment risk greatly influences your personal investment philosophy. Successful investors follow their philosophy. Is your investment philosophy conservative, moderate, or aggressive? Select one philosophy and give your reasons below. (Use with *Personal Finance*, 11th edition, pages 383-388.)

1. My investment philosophy is:

   _____

2. My willingness to accept investment risk is:

   _____

   _____

3. My goals in terms of investment returns are:

   _____

   _____

4. Other things that may characterize my investment philosophy are:

   _____

   _____

5. People with my investment philosophy typically consider investing in the following kinds of investments:

   _____

   _____

6. People with my investment philosophy with $10,000 might expert to have an annual gain of about how much?

   _____

   _____

WORKSHEET 51—MY PREFERRED LONG-TERM INVESTMENT STRATEGIES

Most people are long-term investors who seek genuine growth in the value of their investments that exceeds the rate of inflation, usually for 10 or 15 years or longer. Successful investors exercise discipline and follow one or more long-term investment strategies. For each of the strategies below, identify what one characteristic you like about it, and note which strategies you might follow during your own investing life. (Use with *Personal Finance*, 11th edition, pages 392-402.)

Long-Term Investment Strategies Worksheet

Long-term investment strategies	What one characteristic I like about the strategy	Checkmark each of the strategies I will follow myself
Buy-and-hold		
Portfolio diversification		
Asset allocation		
Dollar-cost averaging		

WORKSHEET 52—MY INVESTMENT GOALS AND TIME HORIZONS

Some typical investment goals are paying off credit card debts, saving and investing to pay for future college tuitions bills, accumulating a down payment to purchase a home, buying a new vehicle, paying for an expensive vacation, and creating a substantial retirement savings nest egg. List below some of your investment goals (one or two for each time period, if appropriate) according to the time horizons when you will need to have accumulated sufficient funds to pay for them. Also identify some possible investments you might consider to achieve those goals. (Use with *Personal Finance*, 11th edition, pages 403-404.)

Investment Goals and Time Horizons Worksheet

Time horizon	My investment goals	Possible investments I might consider
Less than 2 years	1. 2.	
2 to 5 years	1. 2.	
6 to 10 years	1. 2.	
More than 10 years	1. 2.	

WORKSHEET 53—THE REAL RETURN ON MY INVESTMENTS

To identify the real return on your investments, you first need to subtract the negative effects of your marginal tax bracket on the rate of return to obtain the after-tax return. Then you subtract the effects of inflation from the after-tax return. In the appropriate spaces below, insert the rate of return on your investment, your marginal tax bracket, and your estimate of annual inflation. The result is the real return on your investments after taxes and inflation. An interactive calculator that performs this same procedure can be found on the Garman/Forgue companion website. (Use with *Personal Finance*, 11th edition, page 388.)

In the example provided, an investor has an investment opportunity that will pay an 8 percent rate of return. After subtracting the effects of taxes, the investment has an after-tax rate of return of 6 percent (Step 4). Further calculations address the effect of inflation on the rate of return. As a result, the real rate of return on this investment is 3.5 percent (Step 6).

Real Return on Investment Worksheet

(A) Steps	(B) Instructions	(C) Example	(D) Your figures
Step 1	Record the taxable return on the investment.	10%	
Step 2	Record the investor's marginal tax rate.	25%	
Step 3	Subtract the investor's marginal tax rate from 1 (1 – MTR).	0.75	
Step 4	Multiply Step 1 by Step 3 to obtain the investment's after-tax rate of return.	7.5%	
Step 5	Record the current annual inflation rate.	4%	
Step 6	Subtract Step 5 from Step 4 to determine the real return on the investment.	3.5%	

WORKSHEET 54—MY PREFERENCES AMONG STOCKS

There are different classifications of stocks, and these designations can be used to match an investor's preferences. The three basic classifications of stocks are income, growth, and speculative. A number of other terms are used to meaningfully characterize stocks. For each of the types of stocks below that are of interest to you, identify what one characteristic you do or do not like about it, and note those in which you might invest in during your own investing life. (Use with *Personal Finance*, 11th edition, pages 415-419.)

Preferences Among Stocks Worksheet

Stock classifications	What one characteristic I do *or* do not like about this type of stock (but *only* comment below if the stock is of interest to you).	Checkmark in this column each stock that I might invest in.
Income stock		
Growth stock		
Speculative stock		
Blue-chip stock		
Value stock		
Cyclical stock		
Countercyclical stock		

WORKSHEET 55—COMPARING STOCKS AS INVESTMENTS

When you invest in the stock market, you buy shares in companies and become one of their owners. To make good choices, you need to understand some important numbers that are key measures of stock performance. Go online and search out details on key measures of stock performance for two or three companies that are of interest to you as possible investments. Perhaps use Yahoo Finance (biz.yahoo.com/r/) or CNNMoney (money.cnn.com/). Record the information you find on the worksheet below. Then respond to the question that follows: "Which company appears to be the most suitable investment for you, and why?" (Use with *Personal Finance*, 11th edition, pages 419-424.)

Comparing Stocks Worksheet

Key performance measures	Company 1	Company 2	Company 3
Current market price			
Cash dividends			
Dividend payout ratio			
Dividends per share			
Dividend yield			
Book value			
Book value per share			
Price-to-book ratio			
Earnings per share			
Price/earnings ratio			
Price-to-sales ratio			
Beta			
Other measure			
Other measure			
Other measure			
Other measure			

Which company appears to be the most suitable investment for you, and why?

_____

_____

_____

WORKSHEET 56—MY PREFERENCES AMONG BONDS

People invest in bonds to increase their current income. For each of the types of bonds below that are of interest to you, identify what one characteristic you do or do not like about it, and note those in which you might invest in during your own investing life. (Use with *Personal Finance*, 11th edition, pages 439-449.)

Bonds Preference Worksheet

Types of bonds	What one characteristic I do *or* do not like about this type of investment (but *only* comment below if the investment is of interest to you).	Checkmark in this column each investment that I might invest in.
Corporate bond (high quality)		
Corporate bond (junk bond)		
Treasury bond (long-term)		
Treasury note		
I bond		
TIPS bond		
Treasury bill		
Federal agency debt issues		
Municipal bonds		

WORKSHEET 57—COMPARING TAXABLE AND TAX-FREE INCOME

Investors should use a taxable investment's after-tax yield when making comparisons with tax-free alternatives. They should also compare only after-tax yields when two taxable investments are subject to different marginal tax rates. To find out whether a taxable investment pays a higher after-tax yield than a tax-exempt alternative, the investor must determine the after-tax yield of the taxable alternative. In the appropriate spaces below, insert the taxable yield on one investment and your marginal tax bracket. The result is the equivalent after-tax yield on the taxable investment. An interactive calculator that performs this same procedure can be found on the Garman/Forgue companion website. (The formula can be reversed to solve for the equivalent taxable yield when one knows the tax-exempt yield.) Use with *Personal Finance*, 11th edition, pages 388 and 443.

After-tax Return on an Investment Worksheet

(A) Steps	(B) Instructions	(C) Example	(D) Your figures
Step 1	Record the taxable return on the investment.	8%	
Step 2	Record the investor's marginal tax rate.	25%	
Step 3	Subtract the investor's marginal tax rate from 1 (1 – MTR).	0.75	
Step 4	Multiply Step 1 by Step 3 to obtain the investment's after-tax rate of return.	6%	
Step 5	Record the rate of return on the tax-exempt alternative.	6.5%	
Step 6	Select the best alternative from Step 4 and Step 5.	6.5%, the tax-exempt alternative	

WORKSHEET 58–THE CURRENT YIELD ON MY BOND INVESTMENT

The current yield on a bond equals the bond's fixed annual interest payment divided by its current market price. It is a measure of the current annual income expressed as a percentage when divided by the bond's current market price. In the appropriate spaces below, insert the current annual income on a bond and the current market price of the bond. The result of the division is the current yield. An interactive calculator that performs this same procedure can be found on the Garman/Forgue companion website. See Equation 14.5 in *Personal Finance*, 11th edition, page 447.

The current yield can be used to compare two or more bonds with differing market values, coupon rates, and annual interest payments. In the example, a bond that has a coupon rate of 5.5 percent would pay $55 (5.5% x $1,000) and might have a market price of $940. Its current yield would be 5.85 percent.

Current Yield on a Bond Worksheet

(A) Steps	(B) Instructions	(C) Example	(D) Your figures: Bond 1	(E) Your figures: Bond 2
Step 1	Annual interest payment on the bond	$55		
Step 2	Current market price of the bond	$940		
Step 3	Current yield on the bond (Step 1 divided by Step 2)	5.85%		

WORKSHEET 59—THE PRESENT (or CURRENT) VALUE OF MY BOND INVESTMENT

The current market price of a bond depends upon the bond's fixed annual interest payment given current interest rates in the market for bonds with similar levels of risk. In the appropriate spaces below, insert the current annual income on a bond and the current market price of the bond. The result of the division is the current yield. An interactive calculator that performs this same procedure can be found on the Garman/Forgue companion website. (Use with Equation 14.4 in *Personal Finance*, 11th edition, page 447.)

In the example, a bond that has a coupon rate of 6 percent would pay $60 interest (6% x $1,000) in two $30 installments per year. If current interest rates for bonds with similar levels of risk were 8.0 percent, the bond would have a market price of only $802.08.

Current Value of a Bond Worksheet

(A) Steps	(B) Instructions	(C) Example	(D) Your bond
Step 1	Annual interest payment on the bond	$60	
Step 2	Current market interest rates (as a decimal)	8.0%	
Step 3	Years to maturity for the bond	20	
Step 4	Present value of the stream of semi-annual interest payments (see Appendix A.4 for the appropriate interest factor)	$593.78	
Step 5	Present value of the face amount of the bond (see Appendix A.2 for the appropriate interest factor)	$208.30	
Step 6	Current value of the bond (Step 4 plus Step 5)	$802.08	

WORKSHEET 60—THE YIELD TO MATURITY OF MY BOND

The yield to maturity (YTM) is the total annual effective rate of return earned by a bondholder on a bond when it is held to maturity. It reflects both the current income and any difference if the bond was purchased at a price other than its face value spread over the life of the bond. The YTM can be estimated using a math formula (such as Equation 14.6 on page 448 of *Personal Finance*, 11th edition) or using a worksheet such as the one below.

Use the worksheet to calculate the yield to maturity (YTM) on your bond investments. Use Column D in the worksheet to record the figures for your bond (Bond 1), and use Column E if needed. An interactive calculator that performs this same procedure can be found on the Garman/Forgue companion website. (Use with *Personal Finance*, 11th edition, pages xxx-xxx.)

Yield to Maturity (YTM) Worksheet

(A) Steps	(B) Instructions	(D) Your figures: Bond 1	(E) Your figures: Bond 2
Step 1	Record the bond's current market value or price.		
Step 2	Record the bond's face value.		
Step 3	Record the number of years until the bond matures.		
Step 4	Record the amount of annual interest the bond is supposed to pay.		
Step 5	Subtract the amount in Step 1 from the amount in Step 2.		
Step 6	Divide the amount in Step 5 by the amount in Step 3.		
Step 7	Add amounts in Steps 4 and 6; this figure is the average dollar return per year.		
Step 8	Add amounts in Steps 1 and 2.		
Step 9	Divide amount in Step 8 by amount in Step 2.		
Step 10	Divide amount in Step 7 by amount in Step 9; this figure is an estimate of the annual yield to maturity.		

WORKSHEET 61—MY MUTUAL FUND PREFERENCES

Each of the thousands of mutual funds has one of four major objectives: income, balanced, growth, or growth and income. Since people usually have a number of different investment objectives with different time horizons, many investors own all four types of funds. Funds do differ, however, on how they achieve their objectives and this is where investors have to think carefully and make decisions that appropriately fit their investment philosophy. For each of the types of mutual funds below that are of interest to you, identify what one characteristic you like about it, and note those in which you might invest in during your own investing life. (Use with *Personal Finance*, 11th edition, pages 448-467.)

Mutual Fund Preference Worksheet

Mutual fund objectives and fund types	What one characteristic I like about this type of mutual fund. (Only comment below if the fund is of interest to you.)	Checkmark each fund that I might invest in
Income objective— Bond fund		
Income objective— Municipal bond fund		
Balanced objective— Balanced fund		
Growth objective— Growth fund		
Growth objective— Value fund		
Growth objective— Aggressive growth fund		
Growth objective— Small-cap fund		
Growth objective— Sector fund		
Growth objective— Precious metals and gold fund		
Growth objective— Global fund		
Growth objective— International fund		
Growth and income objective— Growth and income fund		
Growth and income objective— Life-cycle fund		
Growth and income objective— Socially conscious fund		
Growth and income objective— Mutual fund fund		

WORKSHEET 62—COMPARING MUTUAL FUNDS AS INVESTMENTS

When you invest in mutual funds, you buy shares in the investment companies and become one of their owners. To make good choices, you need to understand some important numbers that are key measures of fund performance. Go online and search out details on key measures of mutual fund performance for two or three companies that are of interest to you as possible investments. Perhaps use CNN Money (http://money.cnn.com/data/funds/) or Kiplinger Personal Finance (http://kiplinger.com/tools/fundfinder/fundsearch.php/). Record the information you find on the worksheet below. Then respond to the question that follows: "Which mutual fund appears to be the most suitable investment for you, and why?" (Use with *Personal Finance*, 11th edition, pages 467-477.)

Comparing Mutual Funds Worksheet

Key performance measures	Fund 1	Fund 2	Fund 3
Current net asset value (NAV)			
1 year return			
3 year return			
5 year return			
Universe			
Category			
Style			
Decile rank within style			
Last year			
Two years ago			
Three years ago			
Down market			
Volatility rank			
Turnover			
Assets (millions)			
Manager since			
Minimum investment			
Maximum load			
Expense ratio			
Other measure			
Other measure			

Which mutual fund appears to be the most suitable investment for you, and why?

_____

_____

WORKSHEET 63—CALCULATING THE RETURN ON MUTUAL FUND INVESTMENTS

The total return earned by an investor in mutual funds is comprised of income from mutual fund dividends (cash distributions) and capital gains from price appreciation (increases in net asset value [NAV]). Use the worksheet below to calculate your total return on mutual fund investments.

Use Column D in the worksheet to record the figures for your mutual fund (Fund 1), and use Column E if needed. An interactive calculator that performs this same procedure can be found on the Garman/Forgue companion website. (Use with *Personal Finance*, 11th edition, pages 438-477.)

Calculating the Return on Mutual Fund Investments Worksheet

(A) Steps	(B) Instructions	(C) Example	(D) Your figures: Fund 1	(E) Your figures: Fund 2
Step 1	Record the net asset value (NAV) at the beginning of the time period.	$24.00		
Step 2	Record the amount of cash distributions received during the time period.	$1.10		
Step 3	Record the NAV at the end of the time period.	$25.70		
Step 4	Subtract the amount in Step 1 from the amount in Step 3; this figure is the change in NAV.	$1.70		
Step 5	Add amounts in Steps 2 and 4; this is the total return in dollars.	$2.80		
Step 6	Divide the amount in Step 5 by the amount in Step 1; this is the total return during the time period as a percent.	11.67%		

WORKSHEET 64—EVALUATING THE PERFORMANCE (GAIN OR LOSS) OF MY INVESTMENTS

You should evaluate the performance of your investments at least once a year. To do so, use a form like the one below. List the names of your investments, such as stocks, bonds, and mutual funds, in Column 1, the number of shares of securities owned in Column 2, and the purchase prices in Column 3. Multiply the figures in Columns 2 and 3 to obtain the total. Record any purchasing commissions paid in Column 4, and add the figures in Columns 3 and 4 to obtain the total amount you have invested in each investment. Record the current closing prices as of a certain date for each investment in Column 6. Multiply the figures in Columns 1 and 6 to obtain the total closing market value of each investment and record those amounts in Column 7. Subtract the figures in Column 5 from Column 7 to determine the gain or loss, and record those amounts in Column 8. Record any dividends or interest in Column 9. In Column 10, record the total gain or loss for each investment by adding the figures in Columns 8 and 9. Finally, adding all the figures in each column vertically provides totals for all your investments for the reporting period. (Use with *Personal Finance*, 11th edition, pages 380-477.)

Investment Performance (Gain or Loss) Worksheet

Your name: _____

Reporting Period (inclusive dates): _____

Investment	(1) Number of shares	(2) Purchase price per share	(3) Total (1 + 2)	(4) Commission	(5) Total amount invested (3 + 4)	(6) Closing market value	(7) Total closing market value (6 x 1)	(8) Gain or loss (7 – 5)	(9) Dividends, interest, rent	(10) Total gain or loss (8 + 9)
Running Paws (example)	100	$74	$7,400	$148	$7,548	$79	$7,900	$352	$166	$518
Totals										

Gain or loss this reporting period

Dollar return (total of Column 10): (Example $518) _____

Rate of return (dollar return [from line above] divided by total of Column 5):

(Example [$518/$7,548] 6.86%) _____

SECTION FIVE

RETIREMENT AND ESTATE PLANNING

This section of your workbook focuses on mechanisms you will use to create a retirement nest egg and then to pass on your estate to your heirs. Each worksheet will allow you to think through a decision or perform calculations related to a specific area of personal financial management in a way that has direct benefit to you. Worksheets marked with an asterisk can be found on the Garman/Forgue companion website at www.cengagebrain.com.

WORKSHEET 65—HOW MUCH MUST I SAVE FOR RETIREMENT IN TODAY'S DOLLARS

This worksheet will help you calculate the annual amount you need to set aside in today's dollars so that you will have adequate funds for your retirement. The example illustration assumes that a single person is now 35 years old, will retire at age 62, has a current income of $50,000, currently saves and invests about $2,000 per year, contributes zero to an employer-sponsored retirement plan, anticipates needing a retirement income of $35,000 per year assuming a spending lifestyle at 70 percent of current income ($50,000 x .70), and will live an additional 20 years beyond retirement. Investment returns are assumed to be 3 percent after inflation. An interactive calculator that performs this same procedure can be found on the Garman/Forgue companion website. (Use with *Personal Finance*, 11th edition, pages 516-518.)

Retirement Savings Goal Worksheet

Steps	Instructions	Example	Your Numbers
1.	Annual income needed at retirement in today's dollars (Use carefully estimated numbers or a certain percentage, such as 70% or 80%.)	$40,000	_____
2.	Estimated Social Security retirement benefit in today's dollars	$13,200	_____
3.	Estimated employer pension benefit in today's dollars (Ask your retirement benefit advisor to make an estimate of your future pension, assuming that you remain in the same job at the same salary, or make your own conservative estimate.)	$5,800	_____
4.	Total estimated retirement income from Social Security and employer pension in today's dollars (line 2 + line 3)	$19,000	_____
5.	Additional income needed at retirement in today's dollars (line 1 – line 4)	$21,000	_____
6.	Amount you must have at retirement in today's dollars to receive additional annual income in retirement (line 5) for 20 years (from Appendix A.4, assuming a 3% return over 20 years, or 14.8775 x $21,000)	$312,427	_____
7.	Amount already available as savings and investments in today's dollars (add lines 7-A through 7-D, and record total on line 7-E)		
	A Employer savings plans, such as a 401(k), SEP-IRA, or profit-sharing plan	0	_____
	B IRAs and Keoghs	$24,000	_____
	C Other investments, such as mutual funds, stocks, bonds, real estate, and other assets available for retirement	$13,000	_____
	D If you wish to include a portion of the equity in your home as savings, enter its present value minus the cost of another home in retirement	0	_____
	E Total retirement savings (add lines A through D)	$37,000	_____
8.	Future value of current savings/investments at time of retirement (Using Appendix A.1 and a growth rate of 3% over 27 years, the factor is 2.2213; thus, 2.2213 x $37,000)	$82,188	_____
9.	Additional retirement savings and investments needed at time of retirement (line 6 – line 8)	$230,329	_____
10.	Annual savings needed (to reach amount in line 9) before retirement (using Appendix A.3 and a growth rate of 3% over 27 years, the factor is 40.7096; thus, $230,239 ÷ 40.7096)	$5,656	_____
11.	Current annual contribution to savings and investment plans	$1,980	_____
12.	Additional amount of annual savings that you need to set aside in today's dollars to achieve retirement goal (in line 1) (line 10 – line 11)	$3,676	_____

WORKSHEET 66—HOW LONG WILL MY RETIREMENT MONEY LAST?

This worksheet will help you calculate how long your money will last in retirement given a desired withdrawal amount, total nest egg amount and assumed rate of return on the nest egg.   (Use with *Personal Finance*, 11th edition, pages 536-537.)

Insert Your
Figures

Step 1	Amount I Want To Withdraw Annually	
Step 2	Annual Interest Rate I Expect To Earn	
Step 3	The Amount I Have	
Step 4	Divide Step 1 into Step 3	
Step 5	Number of Payments I Can Take (scan down the column in Appendix 1.4 that corresponds to the interest rate in Step 2 for the factor closest to the figure in Step 4. Look across to "n" for that row as an approximation of the number of years your nest egg would last.	

WORKSHEET 67—QUESTIONS TO ASK ABOUT YOUR EMPLOYER'S RETIREMENT PLAN

As you think about your employer's retirement, find out as much as you can. First, identify which type of plan is available. Second, meet with a representative in your employer's human resources department and ask that person the questions indicated by an "X" for that plan; record the answers. (Use with *Personal Finance*, 11th edition, pages 522-527.)

Employer's Retirement Plan Questions Worksheet

Questions to ask	Defined-contribution plan	Defined-benefit plan	Cash balance plan
1. When is an employee eligible to participate in the plan?	X	X	X
2. How much money can the employer and/or employee contribute?	X		X
3. Is the plan optional or required?	X	X	X
4. How are benefits calculated?		X	X
5. Is the plan insured by the Pension Benefit Guaranty Corporation?		X	
6. When does vesting begin?	X	X	X
7. Can the plan be discontinued or changed by the employer and, if so, how?	X	X	X
8. What is the maximum amount that an employee can contribute?	X		X
9. How much of a matching contribution does the employer contribute?	X		X
10. What investment options are available, and under what rules may the employee switch among investment options?	X		X
11. Are the employer's contributions in the form of company stock?	X		X
12. Are participants required to purchase stock in the company with their retirement savings?	X		X
13. What is the formula used to define the full retirement benefit?		X	X

14. What is the normal retirement age?		X	X
15. What is the amount of the retirement benefit?		X	X
16. What is the amount of survivor's benefits, if any?		X	X
17. What is the earliest retirement age?	X	X	X
18. Is the retirement benefit integrated with Social Security and, if so, how?		X	
19. What is the reduction in benefits for early retirement?		X	X
20. Are the retirement benefits guaranteed for life once a person retires?		X	X
21. What are the disability benefits?		X	X
22. At separation from employment or retirement, does the employee have the right to the vested lump-sum amount in the account rather than take a monthly pension?	X	X	X
23. Are the retirement benefits portable, meaning upon termination of employment, an employee can transfer retirement funds from one employer's account to another without penalty?	X	X	X
24. What are the procedures for applying for benefits?	X	X	X
25. Are financial planning services provided to assist employees when making retirement and other financial decisions?	X	X	X

WORKSHEET 68—MY WILL, LETTER OF LAST INSTRUCTIONS, AND ADVANCE DIRECTIVE DOCUMENTS

You may use an advance directive to establish who will make financial, medical, and/or other decisions for you should you become mentally incompetent and/or unable to communicate your wishes. (Use with *Personal Finance*, 11th edition, pages 550-554 and 557-559.)

Will, Letter of Last Instructions, and Advance Directives Worksheet

Document	Date prepared	Document location	Person who knows document location or has copy
Will			
Letter of Last Instructions			
Living Will			
Health Care Proxy			
Durable Power of Attorney			
Limited Power of Attorney			
Other			

WORKSHEET 69—MY ASSETS TO BE TRANSFERRED BY BENEFICIARY DESIGNATIONS

Assigning beneficiaries provides that you as the owner of an asset make certain that the property goes to a certain person(s) and/or organization. When assigning beneficiaries be certain to also assign a contingent (or secondary) beneficiary in case the first-named beneficiary has died. Assets that can be transferred by beneficiary designation include the following. It is smart to retain a photocopy of each assignment form for your personal financial files. (Use with *Personal Finance*, 11th edition, pages 559-560.)

Assets to be Transferred by Beneficiary Designations Worksheet

Asset	Primary beneficiary— name(s)	Contingent beneficiary— name(s)	Date the assignment completed
Life insurance (provided through employer)			
Life insurance (privately purchased)			
401(k) retirement plan at work			
Employer-defined benefit pension plan			
Disability income insurance policy			
IRA—traditional			
Roth IRA			
Checking account (bank or credit union)			
Saving account			
Money market account			
Mutual fund account			
Brokerage account			
Other			